STAR WARS®

THE CLONE WARS™

THE SMUGGLER'S CODE

SCRIPT **JUSTIN ACLIN**   ART **EDUARDO FERRARA**

COLORS **MICHAEL ATIYEH**   LETTERING **MICHAEL HEISLER**

COVER ART **BENGAL**

This story takes place sometime during season 4 of *The Clone Wars*.

...OR SHOULD I CALL YOU *"SHY GUY"*?

I'M NOT SHY, AHSOKA.

IT JUST SEEMS FOOLISH TO BE IN A PLACE LIKE THIS WHEN THERE'S A WAR GOING ON.

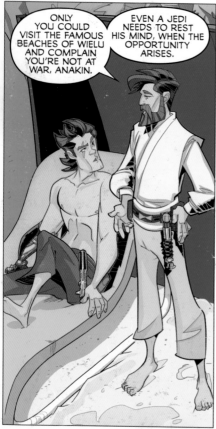

ONLY YOU COULD VISIT THE FAMOUS BEACHES OF WIELU AND COMPLAIN YOU'RE NOT AT WAR, ANAKIN.

EVEN A JEDI NEEDS TO REST HIS MIND, WHEN THE OPPORTUNITY ARISES.

LOOK, YOU TWO HAVE A GREAT TIME. I'M JUST GOING TO GO OUT AND LOOK FOR SOMETHING TO ACTUALLY DO.

I THOUGHT YOU'D GROWN OUT OF THAT IMPULSIVENESS BY NOW.

...I'VE FINALLY GOT YOU.

WHAT IS IT, OBI-WAN?

HOLD THIS FOR ME!

I'LL RECLAIM IT WHEN I'VE FINISHED.

OBI-WAN, I DON'T UNDERSTAND...

OBI-WAN!

11

THIS IS CRAZY, THIS IS CRAZY...

PHEW!

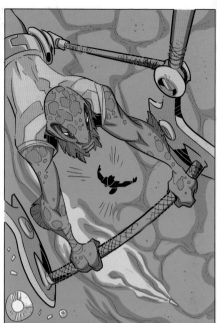

HELLO.

I'M SORRY ABOUT THIS.

CAN I GET YOU SOMETHING, FRIEND?

ACTUALLY...

...I WAS HOPING I COULD INTEREST YOU IN SOMETHING.

R--ROOK! I DIDN'T KNOW IT WAS YOU.

THIS IS THE FINEST NEIMOIDIAN AMBER. IMPOSSIBLE TO GET WITH THE TRADE EMBARGOES...

...BUT I'VE GOT AN ENTIRE HOLD FULL OF IT ON MY SHIP -- FOR A LOW, LOW PRICE.

I'M SORRY, ROOK. TRULY.

BUT THE WORD'S OUT FROM ALL THE BOSSES...NO ONE IS TO DO ANY BUSINESS WITH YOU.

THANKS!

HRNGH.

YOU'RE MINE NOW, T'MOTT.

YOU'LL STAND TRIAL ON HELLEGUTH FOR YOUR CRIMES.

GRRRR...

THERE'S A REPUBLIC TRANSPORT WAITING TO --

NO. I SWORE I'D BRING YOU IN MYSELF.

THAT MEANS I CAN'T INVOLVE MY FRIENDS.

22

LET'S NOT GET GREEDY.

I'LL GIVE YOU A FIVE-MINUTE HEAD START BEFORE I LET HIM GO.

NICE CATCHING UP, KENOBI.

WE'LL HAVE TO DO IT AGAIN IN ANOTHER *TWENTY YEARS!*

YOU DON'T UNDERSTAND WHAT YOU'RE DOING, ROOK.

SURE I DO.

400 CREDITS IS WAY MORE THAN THE GOING RATE FOR A JUMP TO HELLEGUTH.

VSSH

T'MOTT ZOAT! COME OUT AND *FACE ME!*

CAN'T SEE A THING IN THIS...

HA!

SQUAWK!

KSHHH

WELL, NOW I KNOW WHO TO CALL WHEN I HAVE AN OCUVOX INFESTATION.

HAVEN'T YOU DONE ENOUGH DAMAGE ALREADY?

LOOK, I WANT TO MAKE IT UP TO YOU...

KENOBI, IS IT?

OBI-WAN KENOBI.

I DIDN'T REALIZE WHO T'MOTT WAS OR WHY YOU WERE TAKING HIM.

I JUST SAW AN OUTLAW BEING TAKEN IN BY AN AUTHORITY...AND IN THOSE SITUATIONS I USUALLY SIDE WITH THE OUTLAW.

I CAN APPRECIATE THAT, I SUPPOSE.

BUT I'M LOSING GROUND TO T'MOTT EVERY MOMENT, SO IF YOU'LL EXCUSE ME...

YOU WON'T FIND HIM IN THIS JUNGLE, OBI-WAN.

IF YOU'RE LUCKY YOU'LL SURVIVE, BUT YOU WON'T FIND HIM.

31

THIS BLASTER WAS OUTLAWED ON MANDALORE FOR BEING TOO DANGEROUS!

DO YOU HAVE ANYTHING IN MY SIZE, GUTODJ?

MY FAVORITE BLASTER MET WITH AN UNFORTUNATE ACCIDENT TODAY.

AH, ROOK PRYCE! I WISH I COULD SELL TO YOU, BUT I LIKE ALL MY BONES TO REMAIN UNBROKEN.

AND WHO IS THIS MAN OF MYSTERY?

THIS IS MY NEW COPILOT, *UH...* SAL'MA BEN-BOBO.

SORRY, THESE AREN'T FOR SALE...TO YOU OR BEN-BOBO.

THAT'S OKAY, WHAT I REALLY NEED IS SOME INFORMATION.

WE'RE LOOKING FOR A BIG SHISTAVANEN NAMED T'MOTT. DO YOU KNOW WHO HE'S WORKING FOR?

I OWE HIM SOME MONEY.

BRICKA, RIGHT?

BRICKA THOMOR, FRIEND. PURVEYOR OF THE FINEST WEAPONS.

ONLY FORTY CREDITS FOR THIS ONE...

...FIFTY CREDITS FOR THE BLASTER AND THE INFORMATION.

ALL RIGHT...SPILL IT, BRICKA.

THE ONE YOU SEEK HAS BEEN WORKING FOR *BOSS SHON TI'JA.*

YOU CAN FIND HIM IN THE MENAGERIE ON ALEKIE ISLAND.

THANKS. COME ON, BEN-BOBO.

A WORD OF ADVICE, FRIEND...

IF YOU'RE GOING TO DEAL ON WIELU...YOU HAVE TO KNOW WHO YOU'RE DEALING WITH.

NO ONE'S EVER HONORED ME MY ENTIRE LIFE, EXCEPT WHEN I'M TRANSPORTING SOMETHING THEY WANT.

I HONOR THE SMUGGLER'S CODE -- *"GET PAID, AS MUCH AS POSSIBLE."*

WELL, LET'S GO GET T'MOTT, AND I'LL SEE YOU'RE PAID WELL FOR YOUR EFFORTS.

THAT'S EXACTLY WHAT I LIKE TO HEAR, KENOBI.

THERE'S NO ONE HERE!

HOW MUCH DO YOU TRUST THAT BRICKA CHARACTER?

ALMOST NOT AT ALL, BUT A LEAD IS A LEAD.

EXCEPT WHEN A LEAD IS A *TRAP*, OF COURSE!

BRICKA WAS KIND ENOUGH TO LET ME KNOW YOU'D BE HERE, ROOK...

NOW I CAN THANK YOU PERSONALLY FOR SELLING MY WEAPONS TO BOSS CAYLAGOS.

SHON TI'JA!

HAH!

AH, A JEDI!

I'VE ALWAYS WANTED TO MATCH A JEDI AGAINST MY SABERFISH.

SABERFISH?

WHAT'S A SABERFI--

SPLASH!

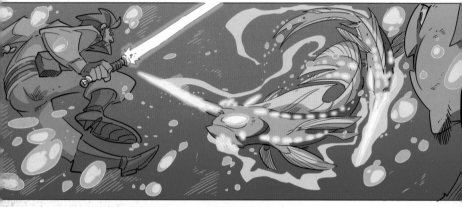

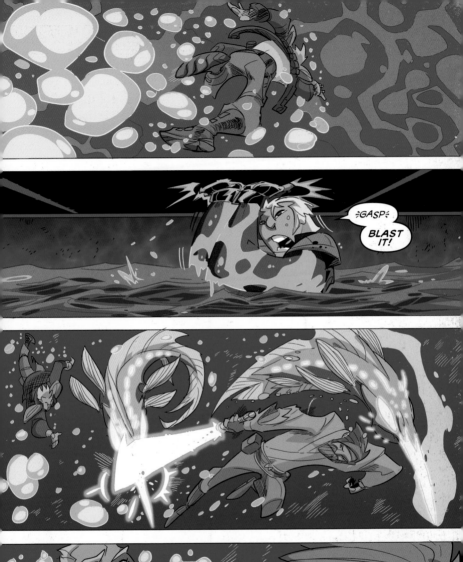

GASP

BLAST IT!

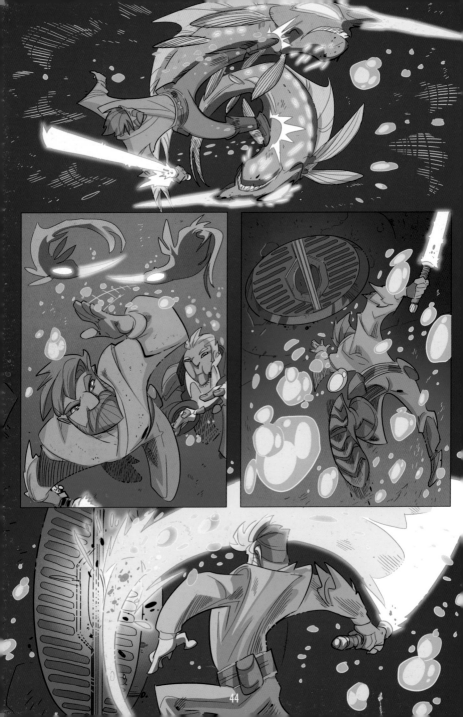

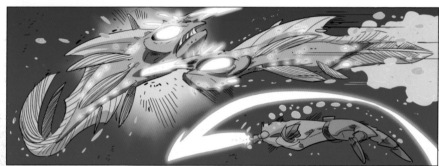

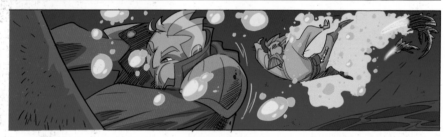

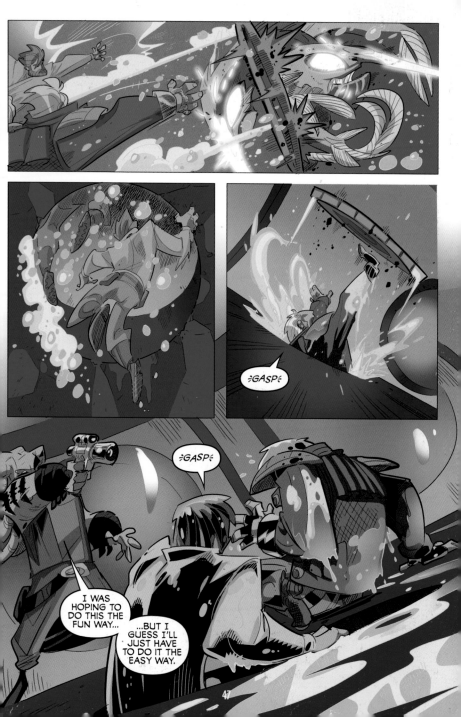

REALLY... NOT IN THE MOOD...FOR GAMES.

ZZZK

VSSSH

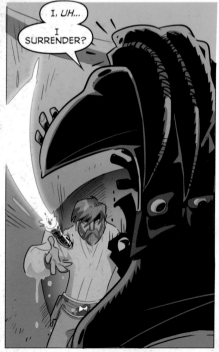

I, UH...
I SURRENDER?

NOW, THEN...

WHERE ARE YOU HIDING T'MOTT ZOAT?

BRICKA WAS LYING... I DIDN'T HIRE HIM!

THEN, DO YOU KNOW WHO DID?

TRAYGURA'S HIDEOUT IS WELL FORTIFIED. WE'LL HAVE TO SNEAK --

ROOK, WAIT...

GETTING FROZEN OUT OF BUSINESS ON WIELU IS ONE THING...

...BUT SHON TI'JA WAS TRYING TO *KILL* YOU!

YOU NEED TO GET OFF THIS PLANET.

IF YOU'RE AS GOOD A PILOT AS YOU ARE WITH THAT BLASTER, I'M SURE THERE'S ROOM FOR YOU IN THE REPUBLIC FLEET.

YOU MEAN IT?

ABSOLUTELY.

WELL, LET'S FIND T'MOTT FOR YOU...THEN WE'LL HAVE A SERIOUS DISCUSSION.

51

NO...THIS WON'T WORK! STICK WITH MY PLAN!

THIS ISN'T A PLAN, OBI-WAN...THIS IS THE SMUGGLER'S CODE. **BOSS TRAYGURA!**

ROOK PRYCE -- DIDN'T I TELL YOU I'D KILL YOU IF I SAW YOU AGAIN?

I COME WITH A GIFT...A HIGH-RANKING JEDI GENERAL IN THE REPUBLIC ARMY.

GRRRR... KENOBI.

LET ME TEAR HIM APART, BOSS.

YOU COULD DO THAT, BUT I'D RANSOM HIM TO THE SEPARATISTS.

THEY'D PAY HANDSOMELY FOR HIM...AND I'LL GET A PIECE OF IT, OF COURSE.

FACE ME, T'MOTT!

GRAAAH!

UNH!

HE HAS TO ANSWER TO OUR FRIEND THAT HE BETRAYED!

THIS OUGHT TO HOLD YOU TWO.

NICELY DONE, SNIPS...

...NOW IF YOU COULD GIVE ME A HAND OVER HERE, I'D REALLY APPRECIATE IT.

YOU COULDN'T CAPTURE ME TWENTY YEARS AGO, KENOBI...

...AND YOU NEVER WILL.

KSSH

HA! ARE YOU *SURE* ABOUT THAT, T'M--

OOF!

OOF!

ANYONE ELSE WANT TO TAKE A SHOT?

LET'S GET *OUTTA* HERE!

WE SHOULD CALL IN THE LOCAL AUTHORITIES TO ARREST EVERYONE.

HERE, I GUESS I CAN GIVE THIS BACK TO YOU NOW.

YOU CAN USE IT TO CALL THEM.

I'M SORRY YOU DIDN'T GET TO REST, ANAKIN.

ARE YOU KIDDING? THIS WAS THE MOST RELAXING THING I'VE DONE IN AGES!

71

SO, I'VE GOT A DANGEROUS CRIMINAL HERE I NEED TO TRANSPORT TO HELLEGUTH.

I DON'T SUPPOSE YOU TWO WOULD BE INTERESTED IN HELPING?

OH, I DON'T KNOW, OBI-WAN. I MEAN, YOU'VE GOT AN OATH TO UPHOLD AND EVERYTHING.

COME ON, AHSOKA... LET'S HIT THE BEACH.

‡SIGH‡

FINE.

ANAKIN, AHSOKA...WILL YOU PLEASE HELP ME ON THIS MISSION?

OF COURSE WE WILL!

BUT YOU'RE SURE YOU DON'T WANT TO HANDLE THIS YOURSELF, LONE WOLF?

NO, NO...

STAR WARS GRAPHIC NOVEL TIMELINE (IN YEARS)

Dawn of the Jedi
36,000 years before
Star Wars: A New Hope

Old Republic Era
25,000–1000 years before
Star Wars: A New Hope

Rise of the Empire Era
1000–0 years before Star
Wars: A New Hope

Rebellion Era
0–5 years after
Star Wars: A New Hope

New Republic Era
5–25 years after
Star Wars: A New Hope

New Jedi Order Era
25+ years after
Star Wars: A New Hope

Legacy Era
130+ years after
Star Wars: A New Hope

Vector
Crosses four eras in timeline

Volume 1 contains:
Knights of the Old Republic Volume 5
Dark Times Volume 3
Volume 2 contains:
Rebellion Volume 4
Legacy Volume 6

Infinities
Does not apply to timeline

Sergio Aragones Stomps Star Wars
Star Wars Tales
Omnibus: Infinities
Tag and Bink
Star Wars Visionaries

BSW4 = before *Episode IV: A New Hope*. ASW4 = after *Episode IV: A New Hope*.

FOR MORE ADVENTURE IN A GALAXY FAR, FAR, AWAY...

**STAR WARS: THE CLONE WARS—
THE WIND RAIDERS OF TALORAAN**
978-1-59582-231-4 | $7.99

**STAR WARS ADVENTURES:
LUKE SKYWALKER AND THE
TREASURE OF THE DRAGONSNAKES**
978-1-59582-347-2 | $7.99

STAR WARS®

CLONE WARS ADVENTURES

Don't miss any of the action-packed adventures of your favorite **STAR WARS®** characters, available at comics shops and bookstores in a galaxy near you!

$6.99 each!

Volume 1	**Volume 2**	**Volume 3**	**Volume 4**	**Volume 5**
ISBN 978-1-59307-243-8	ISBN 978-1-59307-271-1	ISBN 978-1-59307-307-7	ISBN 978-1-59307-402-9	ISBN 978-1-59307-483-8
Volume 6	**Volume 7**	**Volume 8**	**Volume 9**	**Volume 10**
ISBN 978-1-59307-567-5	ISBN 978-1-59307-678-8	ISBN 978-1-59307-680-1	ISBN 978-1-59307-832-4	ISBN 978-1-59307-878-2